What wool of bat is to witches' brew, what the deadly nightshade is to the vegetable kingdom, Charles Addams is to the connoisseur of humor.

Modern science, ahead of us in other sinister matters, has not explained why there is no Addams but Addams, and why evil is his profit.

About the Artist

He was born in Westfield, New Jersey, forty-one years ago and attended Colgate University, the University of Pennsylvania, and Grand Central School of Art in New York City.

His drawings, almost in their entirety, have been published in *The New Yorker*. He works mostly in New York City in what looks like an unsuccessful private eye's office. Practically nothing is accomplished in his house at Westhampton Beach on Long Island. He has owned a series of sports cars and collects medieval crossbows.

Addams daydreams almost constantly and, in his own view, is generally quite lazy.

HOMEBODIES was originally
published by Simon and Schuster.

Other books by Charles Addams

† Addams and Evil
* Black Maria
* Drawn and Quartered
* Monster Rally
* Nightcrawlers

* Published by Pocket Books, Inc.

† To be published by Pocket Books, Inc.

Are there paperbound books you want but cannot find at your retail stores?

HOMEBODIES

Chas Addams

A POCKET **CARDINAL**® EDITION published by
POCKET BOOKS, INC. • **NEW YORK**

HOMEBODIES

Simon and Schuster edition published September, 1954

A Pocket *Cardinal* edition

1st printing.........March, 1965

Of the 90 drawings in this book, the 80 appearing on the following pages
appeared originally in *The New Yorker* and were copyrighted in the respective
years shown by The New Yorker Magazine, Inc.:
PAGES 13, 71, 109 (1950); PAGES 10, 17, 29, 31, 33, 41, 46, 47, 51, 66, 67, 93,
99, 107, 112 (1951); PAGES 8, 9, 18, 19, 23, 25, 26, 27, 32, 34, 37, 44, 45, 49,
52, 57, 59, 61, 62, 63, 65, 92, 95, 128 (1952); PAGES 15, 16, 22, 35, 38, 39, 40,
43, 55, 68, 69, 72-76, 79, 83, 86, 88, 89, 91, 96, 102, 125 (1953); PAGES 11, 21,
54, 77, 80, 81, 85, 101, 104, 111, 113, 114, 115, 117, 120, 122, 127 (1954).

This Pocket *Cardinal*® edition includes every word contained in the
original, higher-priced edition. It is printed from brand-new
plates made from completely reset, clear, easy-to-read type.
Pocket *Cardinal* editions are published by Pocket Books, Inc.,
and are printed and distributed in the U.S.A. by Affiliated Publishers,
a division of Pocket Books, Inc., 630 Fifth Avenue, New York, N.Y. 10020.
Trademarks registered in the United States and other countries.

L

"Now, remember—act casual."

"Nothing much, Agnes.
What's new with you?"

"Mr. Mitchell!
You <u>know</u> you don't have
kitchen privileges."

"Sanders speaking.
Stop all production of XP 15,
recall all shipments,
wire every doctor in the country,
and <u>hurry</u>!"

"All right, children, a nice big sneer, now."

"I'm sorry, sonny. We've run out of candy."

"You forgot the eye of newt."

"There's an amusing little legend connected with it—something about a dreadful curse."

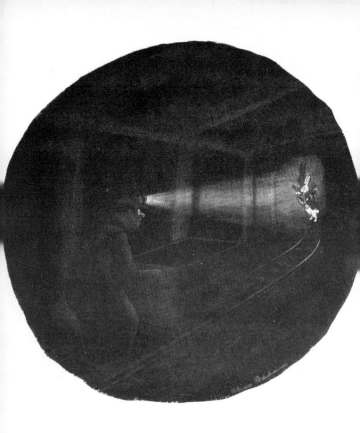

"Now don't tell me you had anthropologist for lunch."

"I should think Alice
would at least be on hand
to help you move."

27

"It's priceless.
Normie's building a rocket
to shoot Pamela to the moon."

"And this is your Uncle Cosimo,
a man of whom it may be truly said
he left the world a little worse
for his having lived in it."

"One thing I'll say for him—
he's always been a good provider."

"What light you giving it?"

"Would you care to
step in here and see
how it looks in the dark?"

"You've never felt that way about me."

"The little dears!
They still believe
in Santa Claus."

"Excuse me, sir,
but are you the Arthur Johnson
who lost this diary?"

54

"You're going to shoot
a hundred and fourteen, dear."

"Well, I don't see any point
in looking any farther.
It was probably just
one of those wild rumors."

"Just the kind of day
that makes you feel
good to be alive!"

"For heaven's sake, Ed,
holler something besides 'help.'
People might think
we're really in trouble."

"I like them. They <u>wear</u> well."

"Something in sneakers?"

"Delmonico's—and hurry!"

". . . then good old Scrooge,
bless his heart,
turned to Bob Cratchit and snarled,
'Let me hear another sound from <u>you</u>
and you'll keep <u>Christmas</u>
by losing your situation.'"

→

"Death ray, fiddlesticks!
Why it doesn't even slow them up."

"It's very interesting, but I'm afraid we only publish science <u>fiction</u>."

"Go right ahead, Pomfret.
The entries closed two weeks ago."

"Everything happens to <u>me</u>."

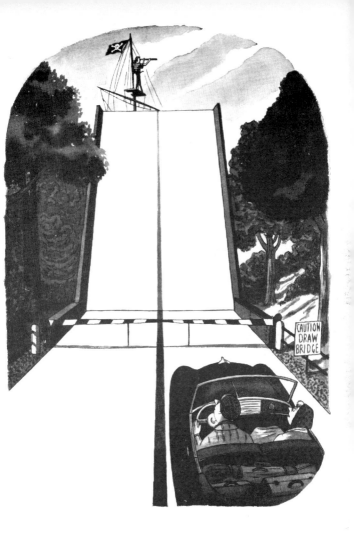

"I give up, Robert. What does have two horns, one eye, and creeps?"

"Then the dragon
gobbled up the handsome young prince
and his lovely bride and
lived happily ever after."

"Oh, for goodness' sake,
forget it, Beasley.
Play another one."

"Well, good night, Ahmed.
If you need anything,
just rub."

"And now we present 'Mary and Bill,'
the story of a family that might be
your next-door neighbors,
and of their everyday life
among everyday people
just like yourselves . . ."

"Wouldn't you know
that at a time like this
Haley would be off somewhere
photographing some damn ritual?"

"Mom, can I have the broom tonight?"

"I have a question
from a lady in Astoria.
She wants to know the best
method of removing bloodstains
from a broadloom rug."

"Have you got a minute, Dr. Headley?
We think we may have found
a new carnivorous specimen."

"All right, now, a little smile."